So you want to have FUN WITH SCRABBLE?
Welcome to the book that shows you how!

If you've got a Scrabble set, get it out and use your letters and board to do the puzzles. If you don't have a set, you could make letters using paper or card. Ask an adult to help you!

Throughout the book are pages of Scrabble game situations to think about and to try.

You'll find the answers to the puzzles at the back of the book, and a list of special **2-letter** words.

Watch out for Top Tips.
Read them and memorize them!
You'll soon be a top player.

The ⛛ symbol means an explanation of a rule.
First, however, make sure you've read the rules of Scrabble... and then good luck with the book!

TAKE YOUR LETTERS

When you've taken your 7 letter tiles from the bag, put them one by one on your rack. Sometimes words will appear before your very eyes. They will jump out at you... spelled out... all ready to be put on the board.

Take this rack for example:

JOKE is staring at you... 4 letters, 2 of them valuable. A good word in itself, but if you move the **D** along a few places, you have **JOKED**... even better!

On the other hand, if you look at this rack, nothing exactly jumps out at you:

But look closer.

Without you moving a single tile, two **4-letter** words are there... spelled out, but with gaps.

HJYOMIN and **HJYOMIN**

CHAMBERS

FUN
WITH
SCRABBLE®

Jim Reid

CHAMBERS

Scrabble® is a registered trademark owned throughout the world by J W Spear & Sons PLC, Leicester, England, a Mattel Company, with the exception of the USA where it is owned by Hasbro Inc. and Canada, where it is owned by Hasbro Canada Inc.

Scrabble® game © 1988, J W Spear & Sons PLC

CHAMBERS
An imprint of Chambers Harrap Publishers Ltd
7 Hopetoun Crescent
Edinburgh
EH7 4AY

A CIP catalogue record for this book is available from the British Library.

ISBN 0 550 14180 4

Author: Jim Reid
Consultant Editor: Catherine Schwarz
Publishing Manager: Elaine Higgleton
Jacket Design: Ian Butterworth

Typeset by Chambers Harrap Publishers Ltd
Printed in Great Britain by Bath Colour Books Ltd

Can you spot the **4-letter** words in each of these racks? Without the tiles being moved, the letters are in the correct order, but with the gaps between.

and

and

There's even a **5-letter** word.

Can you spot it?

Here's a clue to help!

Mostly, however, you will have to give your letter tiles a good old shuffle. Keep them moving and, magically, words will appear. Use tiles from your set to make this rack:

See if you can find these 10 words. There are clues to help.

☐☐☐ a colour		☐☐☐☐ a room entrance
☐☐☐ a female deer		☐☐☐☐ a heathery hill
☐☐☐ a farmyard sound		☐☐☐☐ a wind instrument
☐☐☐ a cosy place		☐☐☐☐ a long gown

☐☐☐☐☐ a brush made from twigs

☐☐☐☐☐ an American cowboy show

Well done if you managed them, and brilliant if you can spot two **7-letter** words!

☐☐☐☐☐☐☐ a part of a house

☐☐☐☐☐☐☐ not having anything to do

Can you make any more words?

4

Notice that you can make **ROME**, the capital city of Italy, and **ROMEO**, a character from one of William Shakespeare's plays. These, however, are spelled with a capital first letter and are not allowed in Scrabble. You cannot play any proper names such as the names of people, countries, continents, seas and planets.

Have a go with these letters:

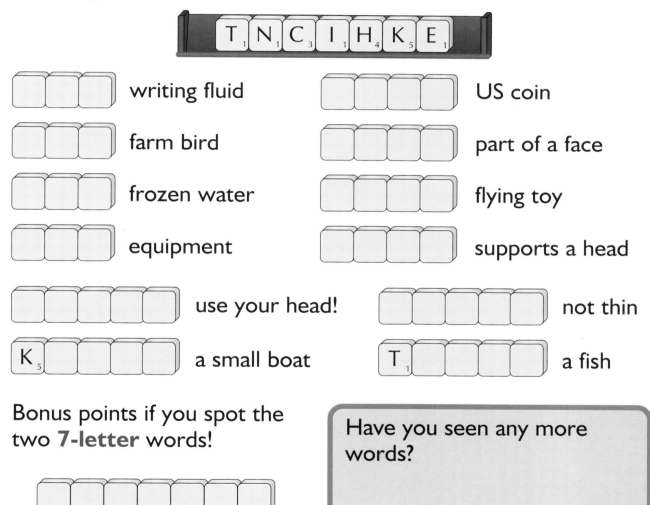

T₁ N₁ C₃ I₁ H₄ K₅ E₁

writing fluid

farm bird

frozen water

equipment

US coin

part of a face

flying toy

supports a head

use your head!

not thin

K₅ ___ a small boat

T₁ ___ a fish

Bonus points if you spot the two **7-letter** words!

another room in the house

to make less thin

Have you seen any more words?

5

TOP TIP

Always give your letter tiles a good shuffle and watch the words appear... hopefully.

Try and spot words with more than 4 letters. You may even find a 7-letter word which is worth 50 bonus points.

TOP TIP

Sometimes, of course, you may pick up a very difficult rack of letters. Take this one for instance:

You could shuffle them from now until doomsday and you wouldn't find any **4-, 5-, 6-,** or **7-letter** words. But, there are a few **3-letter** words. Can you find them?

| point at | a bird | a sweet food | able to | tropical vegetable |

Scrabble RULE

You are allowed to play 2-letter words (more about those later) and in this rack you will see AM, MA, and MY, but not I'M, which has an apostrophe ('), which disallows it for Scrabble.

6

Here's another awkward rack for you. There's not much here either, but if you shuffle the tiles you may find a farm animal, part of a candle and a Chinese cooking dish. (Clue: there's a **W** in each word.)

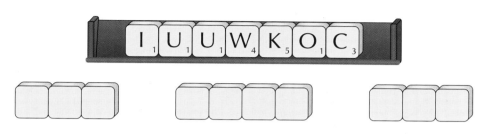

Scrabble Facts

Earlier names were 'Criss Cross Words' and 'Logo-Loco' before 'Scrabble' was chosen.

Scrabble was introduced into Britain in 1954.

French Scrabble has 5 letters worth 10 points (K,W,X,Y,Z).

There are 225 small squares on the board and 100 tiles in a set.

The Portuguese game contains 120 tiles, and the Z is only worth 1 point.

There's a lot about premium squares in the next few pages. These are the Double Letter, Triple Letter, Double Word and Triple Word squares that can help you score more points when tiles are played on them for the first time.

TOP TIP

FIRST MOVE!

The first word played in every game must have one of its letters covering the board's centre starred square — which doubles the first word's score automatically.

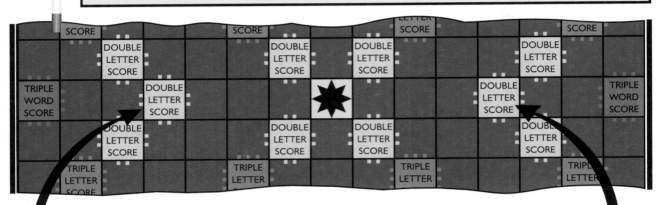

You can play a word downwards (vertically) across the star, but in this book we will always start crossways (horizontally).

TOP TIP

Try, if you can, to play a 5-letter (or longer) word to reach one of the two Double Letter squares on the left and right of the star.

You are opening the game. This is your rack:

You can make **CAN**, **CANE**, **NICE**, but suddenly you see an excellent **5-letter** word beginning with **J**. Can you spot it? (It's something in an orange or lemon.)

You've got it! Now, where do you play it?

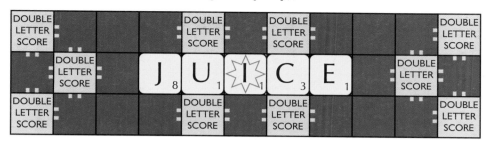

This does not cover a **Double Letter** square.
Score: $8+1+1+3+1=14 \times 2=28$

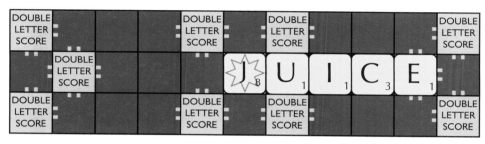

This covers a **DL** square, but the wrong one. Only the **E** (a low-scoring letter) is doubled.
Score: $8+1+1+3+2=15 \times 2=30$

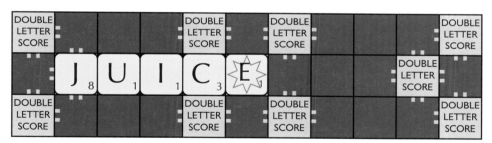

You've put the valuable **J** on a **DL** square.
Score: $16+1+1+3+1=22 \times 2=44$! Much better!

Try and place a high-value letter on a DL square.

Think where you would place these words on your first move, making sure the high-value letters cover a **DL** square.

QUEEN   AFFIX   ZEBRA   QUICK   LAUGH   INDEX

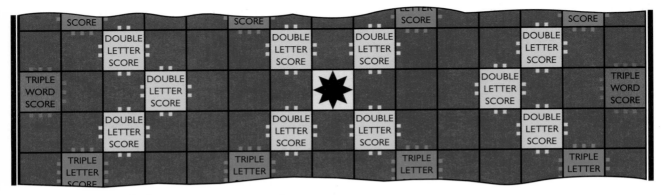

These are all first move racks.

See if you can find the **5-letter** word in each rack and then place it in the best position on your own board.

Clue: abracadabra   Target score: 32

Clue: take it easy   Target score: 40

Clue: duck   Target score: 60

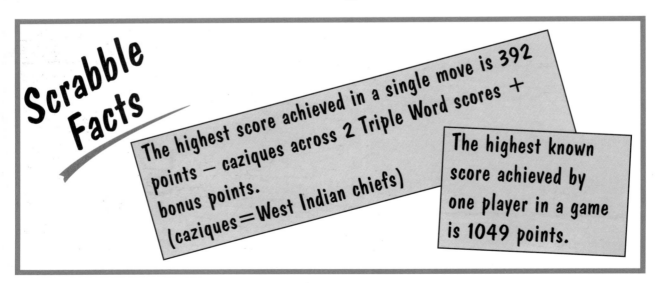

Scrabble Facts

The highest score achieved in a single move is 392 points — caziques across 2 Triple Word scores + bonus points. (caziques = West Indian chiefs)

The highest known score achieved by one player in a game is 1049 points.

This time, aim for a **6-letter** word in each rack, but make sure the high-value letter is placed on a **DL** square.

Clue: medal   Target score: 54

Clue: a short time   Target score: 32

Clue: teacher's hands!   Target score: 46

Think where you would place these words, making sure the high-value letters are placed on **DL** squares.

UNLIKE   BREEZE   AZALEA*   FJORDS#   GALAXY
SKATED   EQUATE°   ALWAYS

* a flower   # deep sea inlets   ° make equal

Have a look at this rack:

Now see if you can work out the **7-letter** word... and place it in the correct position to make:

(30 x 2) = 60
+ 50 bonus points
= 110pts
A very good first move! Magic!

PUZZLE BREAK

Place the letters in the crosses so that each contains 2 words, one down and one across.

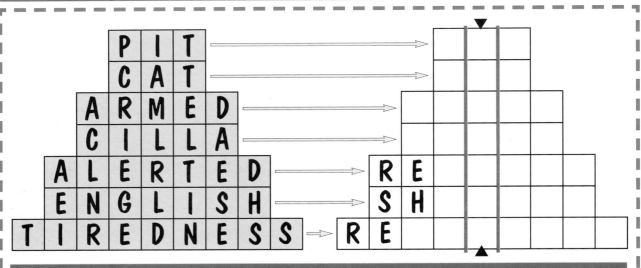

Jumble the words in the left-hand pyramid and place new words in the empty one. You will reveal a country down the ladder.

? ? S T J N M D L C ? ? ?
? ? G E Y P R A O W ? ? ?

The answer to each quiz question below begins with a different letter. Cross these out from the above list and you will be left with 6 letters. Jumble these to spell a musical instrument.

1 What is the capital of New Zealand?

2 Which is the middle colour of a rainbow?

3 Which is the Solar System's largest planet?

4 Dodie Smith wrote a book called 'A Hundred and One - - - - - - - - - -'.

5 Who is the Patron Saint of Scotland?

6 Can you name a London railway station that is also the name of a famous bear?

7 Jumble 'CATHY' to give a small sailing boat.

8 Which large island lies beyond the toe of Italy?

9 Can you name a small red and black spotted insect?

10 What is the name of Earth's only natural satellite?

A CLUELESS CROSSWORD
Jumble the letters for each number across and down and write the words in the grid.

ACROSS	DOWN
1 WLJEE	1 KOJDE
4 TDHCI	2 LUHGA
5 ACMLE	3 PTSAM
7 EHGDE	5 HCTAC
	6 VELAE

● Marked letters will spell an animal.

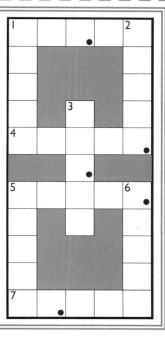

13

SECOND MOVE!

The simplest second move is to add one or more letters to the beginning or end of the word that has been played. Look at this example:

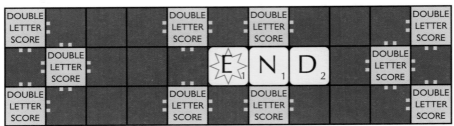

Before **END** you could add:

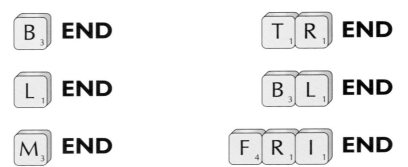

Join each of the letters in the long columns to the beginnings of the words... but only if in doing so a new word is made.

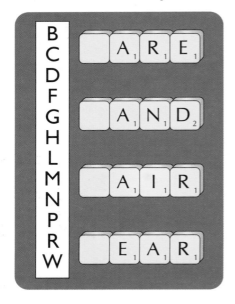

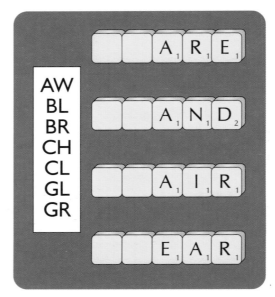

You can also add one or more letters <u>after</u> the word that has already been played:

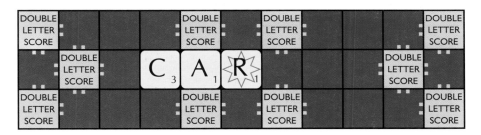

Fill in the **spaces** with letters which will make new words starting with **CAR**. (A dictionary may help.)

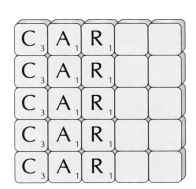
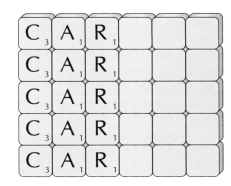

Now try these starting with **FOR**:

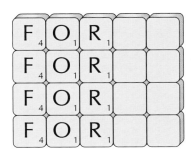

Never use an [S] or a [ ] when just making one word longer. It is a waste of these very useful tiles as you will find out later.

Of course, you can also add letters at each end of a word.

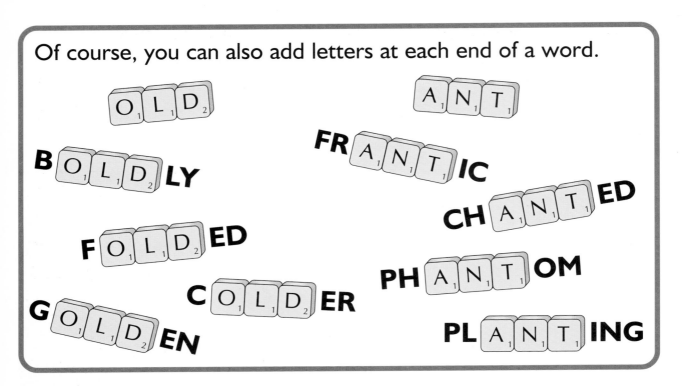

Try adding the given letters to each of these words that have already been played.

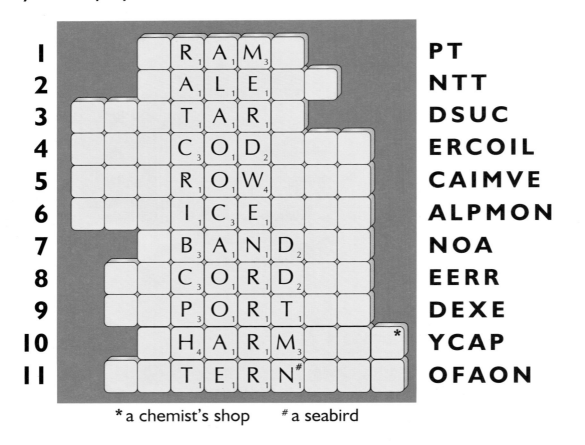

1		R A M								PT
2		A L E								NTT
3		T A R								DSUC
4		C O D								ERCOIL
5		R O W								CAIMVE
6		I C E								ALPMON
7		B A N D							NOA
8		C O R D							EERR
9		P O R T							DEXE
10		H A R M				*			YCAP
11		T E R N#							OFAON

*a chemist's shop   #a seabird

16

Another way of making a new word is by playing letters downwards to the already-played word. In this example, **TREND** has been played, so the second player could play words down any of the arrowed lines with words ending in each of the letters **TREND**.

Suppose this is your rack:

You get the best scores using **Double Word** squares.

The other words are a waste of high-value letters, especially **BAKE** which has the high-scoring **B** and **K** on poor squares.

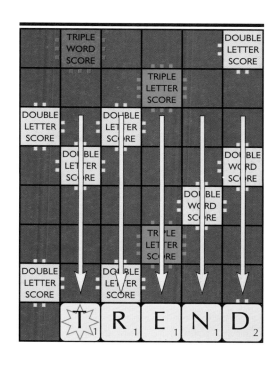

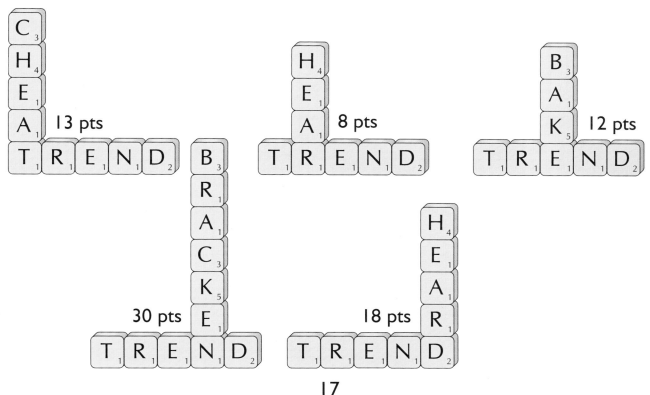

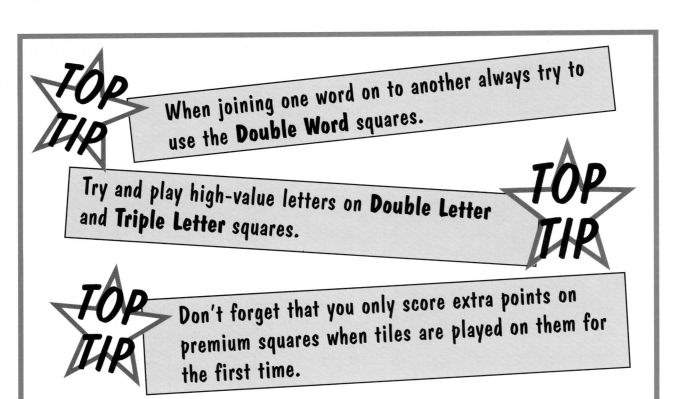

TOP TIP
When joining one word on to another always try to use the **Double Word** squares.

TOP TIP
Try and play high-value letters on **Double Letter** and **Triple Letter** squares.

TOP TIP
Don't forget that you only score extra points on premium squares when tiles are played on them for the first time.

Use the letters in this rack to make words ending with each of the letters of **HELP**.

See if you can reach the target score for each line.

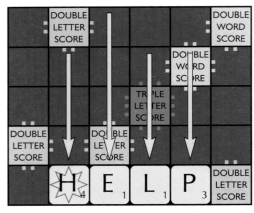

Target scores ⟶ 11 pts 17 pts 9 pts 30 pts

18

Try again with this rack, this time making words ending in the five letters of **KNEEL**.

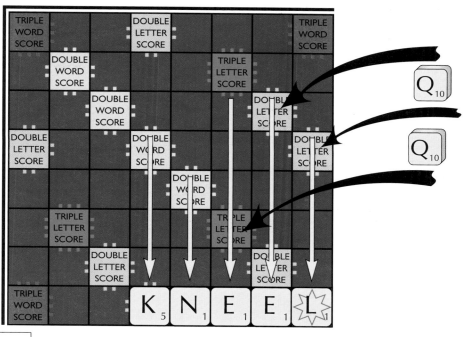

Target scores $\longrightarrow$ 40ₚₜₛ 26ₚₜₛ 40ₚₜₛ 34ₚₜₛ 24ₚₜₛ

When you've got **Q** and **U** on your rack, you're really in business!

All the words above have **QU** in them. Try to get the **Q** on the **DL** and **TL** squares.

Don't worry if you have a **Q** but no **U**. There are several words with a **Q** and no **U**, such as **qintar** (an Albanian unit of currency) and **qasida** (a formal Arabic poem of praise or mourning).

You can also play a word downwards from an already-played word on any of the five lines shown.

Suppose this is your rack:

You could play:

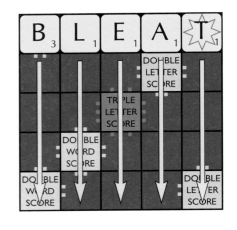

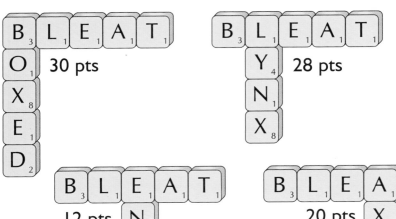

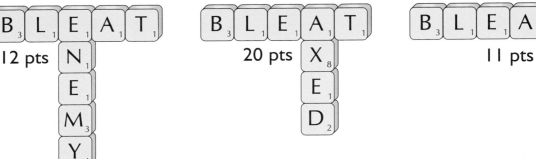

Again, the words formed on the **DW** lines produce the highest scores.

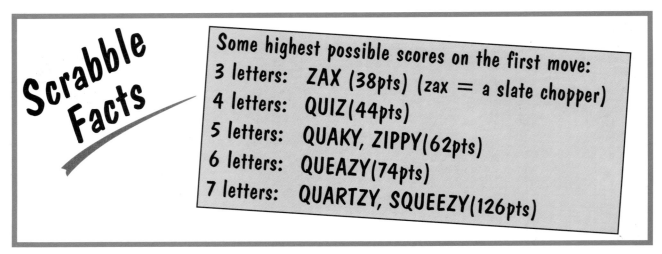

Try this rack with words played downwards from each of the letters of **CAMP**.

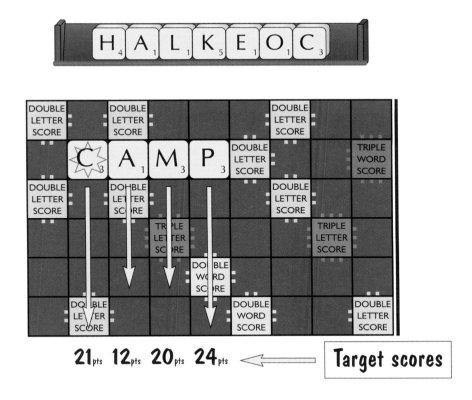

21pts 12pts 20pts 24pts ← Target scores

See if you can reach the target score for each word.

Try to play the **K** on the **DL** and **TL** squares. Notice that the **DW** line has the highest target score.

Scrabble Facts

It has not proved possible to play Scrabble in Japanese or Chinese, but people in Japan and China play in English with a rule book in their own language.

Scrabble is currently produced in 30 languages including a special Braille version.

The last way of forming just one word in a move is to play downwards through an already-played word.

Supposing this is your rack:

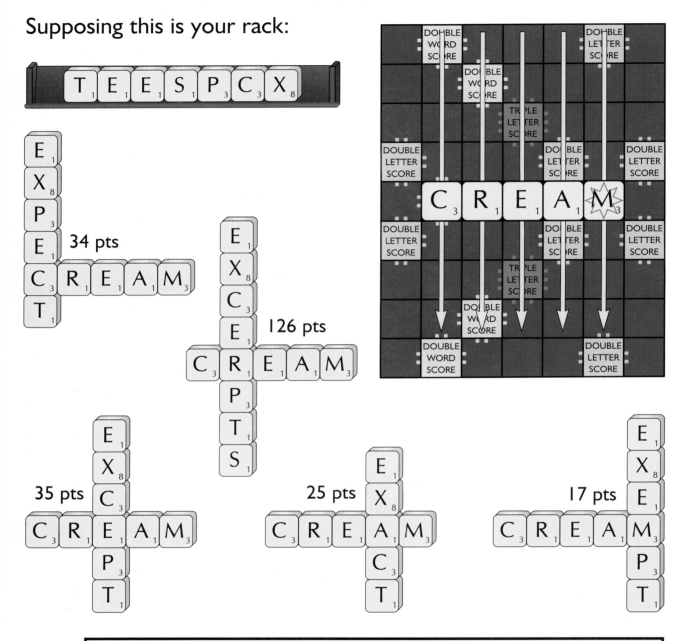

34 pts

E X P E C T — C R E A M

126 pts

E X C E P T S crossing C R E A M

35 pts

E X C P T crossing C R E A M

25 pts

E X A C T crossing C R E A M

17 pts

E X E M P T crossing C R E A M

Scrabble RULE

Notice that on the very high-scoring line of 126 points 50 BONUS POINTS were earned by playing all the letters in one move.
TWO DW score squares were covered in one move, therefore multiplying the letter score by 4!

Notice, too, that we avoided wasting the **S** at the end of all the words other than **EXCERPTS**, where it was used to reach the second **DW** square and to score the bonus 50 points.

Try this rack and see if you reach the target score on each line.

Once again, the highest scores will use the **DW** squares.

Target scores ⟹ **14**pts **12**pts **18**pts **38**pts **20**pts

PUZZLE BREAK

Jumble the letters for each box to make 4 words, 2 words across and 2 words down, in each grid.

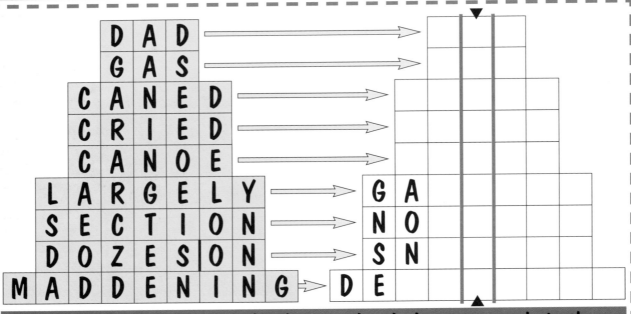

Jumble the words in the left-hand pyramid and place new words in the empty one. You will reveal a flower down the ladder.

Puzzle Letters

X N C Q G E H L W D

A J R S V P O B Z H

? ? ? ? ? ? ?

The 2 words which answer each quiz question below begin with different letters. Cross these out from the above list and you will be left with 6 letters. Jumble these to spell a colour.

1 Who was the famous playwright who wrote 'Macbeth'?

2 Who was the author of 'Oliver Twist' and 'Nicholas Nickleby'?

3 Which two Scrabble letters are worth 8 points each?

4 Can you name the famous black and white comic movie pair — Stan ------ and Oliver ----- ?

5 Which are the Sun's closest two planets?

6 Can you name the long-running children's TV show which is also the name of a naval flag?

7 Which two Scrabble letters are worth 10 points each?

ANOTHER CLUELESS CROSSWORD

Jumble the letters for each number across and down and write the words in the grid.

ACROSS

1 VELEL

4 JONAB

6 XASE

7 NROCA

8 BITHA

9 TOIN

10 GNIEB

11 VEDSA

DOWN

2 ACDEUTE

3 GNINAEL

4 OHIBSPS

5 UBLJIEE

MAKING TWO WORDS IN ONE MOVE

On page 22 we looked at how to play letters **TEESPCX** through **CREAM**.

One of the moves even made 126 points!

Another very profitable move would be to hook a word before or after **CREAM**, making 2 new words at once. This can be done if an already-played word can be lengthened at its beginning or end.

CREAM can become **SCREAM** or **CREAMS**.

Look at these examples and don't forget to score for both new words made in one move and see how well the premium squares are being used.

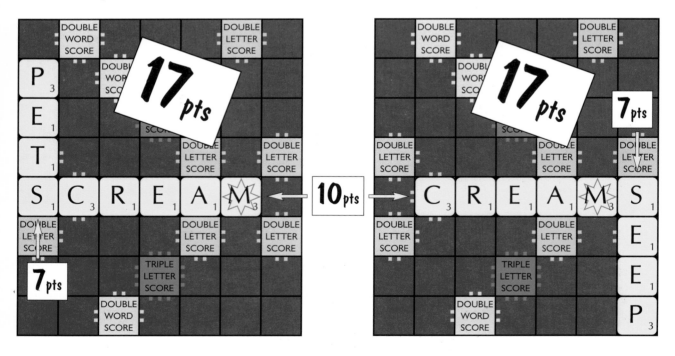

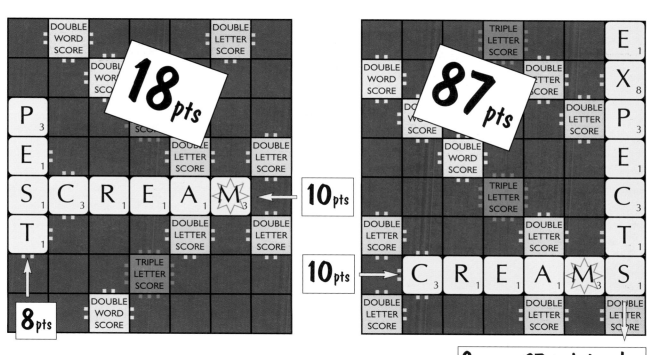

Scores 27 points plus
50 bonus points

Scores 38 points plus
50 bonus points

TOP TIP

Whenever you get the chance, try making 2 words in one move, by hooking your word on to another. This gives you points for 2 words in one move!

Try this example of hooking using the rack below. See if you can reach the target score, not forgetting to score both words.

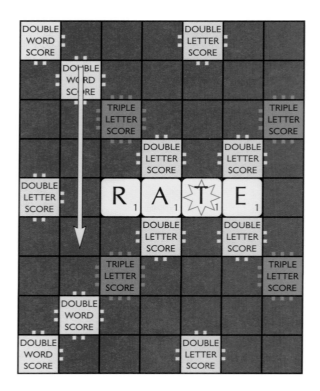

Target score $\left(\downarrow = 26_{pts} \right) + \left(\rightarrow = 7_{pts} \right) = \boxed{33_{pts}}$

This time, try hooking a word on the end of the first word... again making 2 new words. Can you reach the target score? No clues this time!

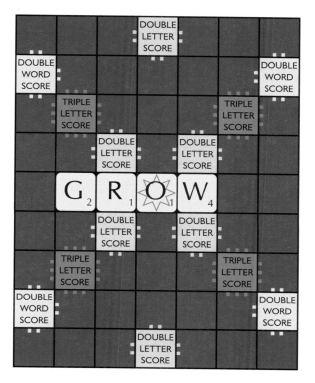

Target score $9_{pts} + 39_{pts} =$ **48**$_{pts}$

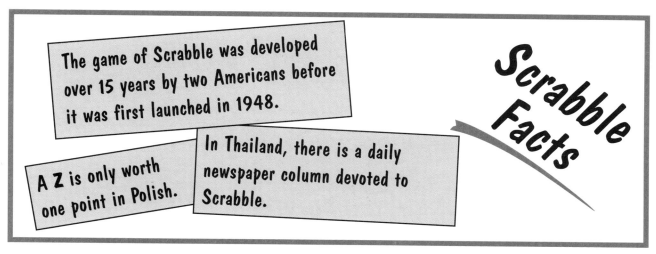

Scrabble Facts

The game of Scrabble was developed over 15 years by two Americans before it was first launched in 1948.

A **Z** is only worth one point in Polish.

In Thailand, there is a daily newspaper column devoted to Scrabble.

Hooking is very common in Scrabble. Try filling in the empty boxes in these examples, making 2 new words every time.

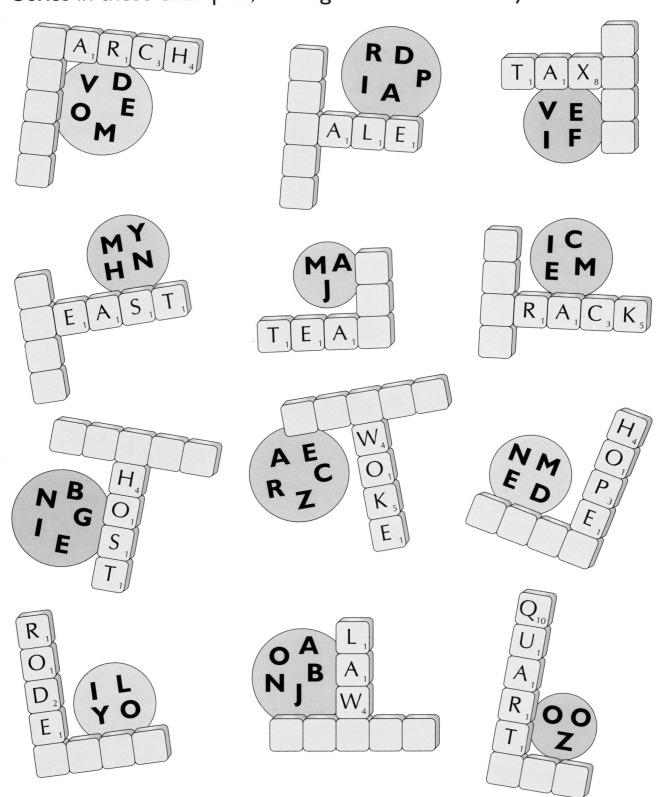

Use **S** as a hooking letter. There are only 4 in a set, so save them for hooking. Never waste an **S**.

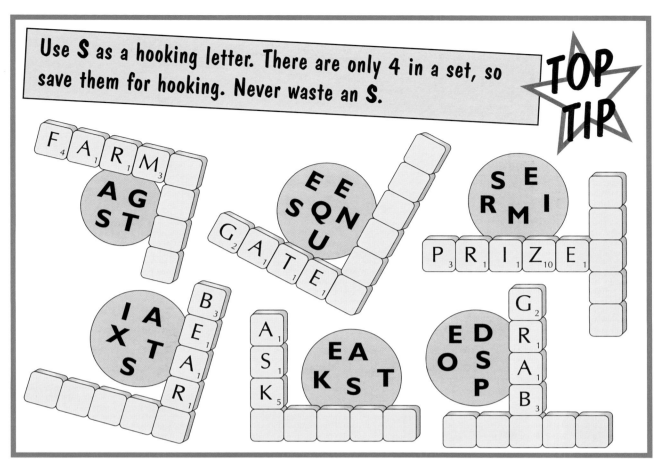

Use blank tiles for hooking as well. There are only 2 in a set, so save them for hooking, or for using as a **U** with a **Q**.

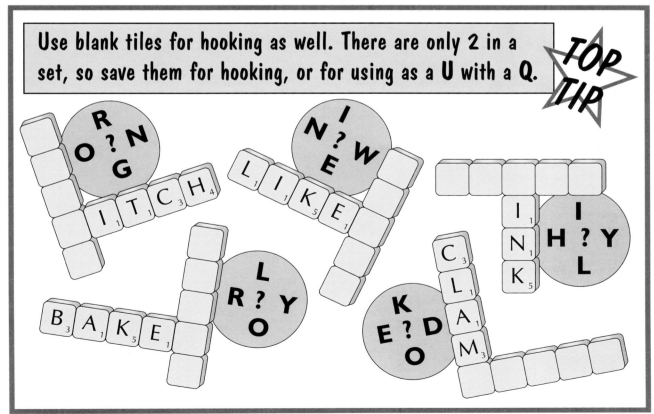

Hooking words is very profitable, especially when the joining square is coloured (**DL**, **TL**, **DW** and **TW**).

Follow this game:

| Player 1 | **HOP** (16pts) | Player 2 | **LAMP** (8pts) |
| Player 1 | **FLAN** (15pts) | Player 2 | **????** (43pts) |

Can you make Player 2's move? It's worth 43 points.

Here is the rack:

Look at that valuable **TL** score square. You'll need to use it carefully to make 43 points.

See if you can work out the next move in this game:

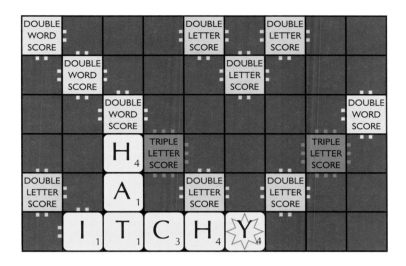

Player 1   **ITCHY** (28pts)   Player 2   **HAT** (6pts)
Player 1   ?????   (44pts)

Can you match the 44 points?

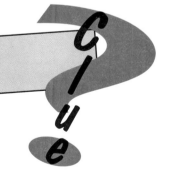

You need to find a way of hooking **W** on to **HAT**.

Player 1 could have scored 34 points on her first move. Can you see how?

(Remember to try to put high-scoring letters on the valuable **DL** and **TL** squares to make as many points as possible.)

Now try this one. Player 1 has spotted a golden opportunity to cash in on the exposed **Triple Word** score square at the top. Can you make the move and score 2 **TW** scores at once? The move is worth 84 points!

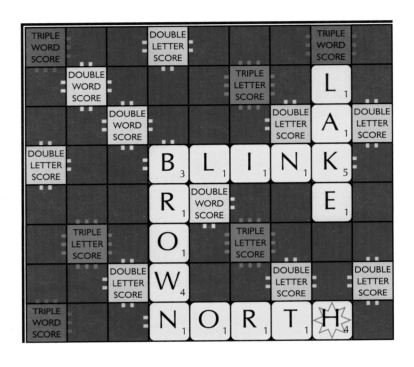

Player 1	**NORTH** (18pts)	Player 2	**BROWN** (20pts)
Player 1	**BLINK** (16pts)	Player 2	**LAKE** (8pts)
Player 1	**?????** (84pts)		

Player 2 certainly made a mistake by leaving the **TW** square open for his opponent.

Player 1's first move could have been worth 24pts.

Can you see how?

TOP TIP If possible, don't play a word which leaves a premium square open for your opponent to hook on to.

Let's look again at all the ways to play a new word on to a word that's already on the board.

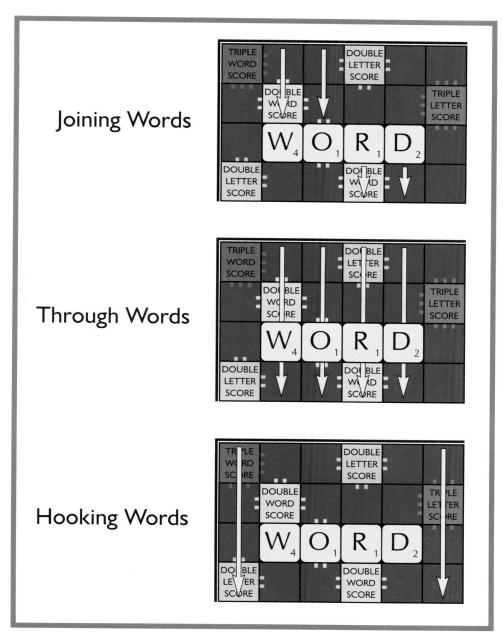

Joining Words

Through Words

Hooking Words

PUZZLE BREAK

Make 3 words in each shape using these letter tiles from your set.

Use the clues to change the word on the left into a new word on the right. Both words have the same letters.

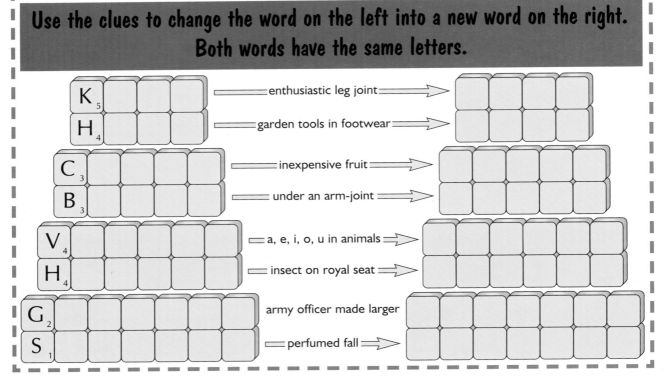

- enthusiastic leg joint
- garden tools in footwear
- inexpensive fruit
- under an arm-joint
- a, e, i, o, u in animals
- insect on royal seat
- army officer made larger
- perfumed fall

TRBAOIATN = TR A O I A N / B O AT

Can you spot the 2 merged words in each set of letters? One letter is not used in each set. Put these in the last boxes and then jumble them to make a sport.

= **DTAUBILSIYP** / _____ FLOWERS

= **SPCAURRMLPETLE** / _____ COLOURS

= **ARTOBHRIUSNH** / _____ BIRDS

= **GIRDARBABFITFE** / _____ MAMMALS

= **VPIELNUUTSO** / _____ PLANETS

= **NAOUCGTUOBSTER** / _____ MONTHS

= **BBARCEAODNT** / _____ FOODS

= **SPBERUEOCCHE** / _____ TREES

= **ACPHRNEIRRCOYT** / _____ FRUITS

_____

Jumble the letters in each sector to make the name of a kind of bird.

Put the first letter of each bird in the middle spaces — to spell another!

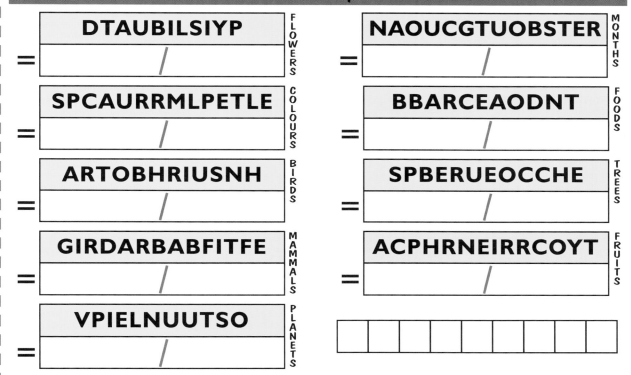

We've found that one way of making 2 words in one move is to hook a new word on to an already-played word.

Another way is by tagging, using **2-letter** words. Tagging is playing a word parallel to (in the same direction as) a word already played. You wouldn't think that tiny **2-letter** words would be worth playing, but they can be the greatest weapon of a Scrabble champion.

Look at this game.

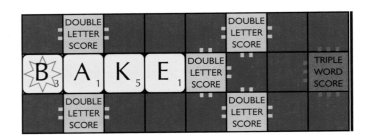

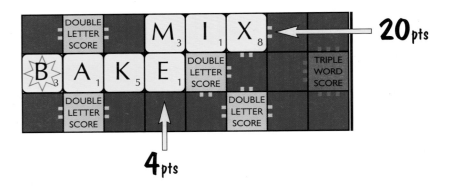

Player 1 has opened with **BAKE**.

Player 2 then decides to tag **MIX** on to **BAKE** making the two words, **ME** (4pts) and **MIX** (20pts).

Total score: 24pts

(Player 2 had spotted that the valuable **X** could be placed on a premium square.)

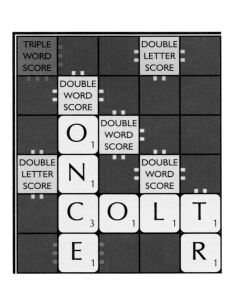

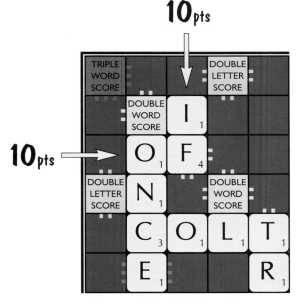

In this game, a player tags **IF** down to a **Double Word** score square (10pts). This also scores **OF** across as a **Double Word** score (10pts).

Total Score: 20pts

You may think that there are not many **2-letter** words, but surprisingly there are over 100.

Here is a list of 40 common **2-letter** words to be found in *The Chambers Dictionary* and all of them are allowable in a game of Scrabble. (More later!)

AD	AT	GO	IF	MA	OH	OY	UM
AH	BE	HA	IN	ME	ON	PA	UP
AM	BY	HE	IS	MY	OR	SH	US
AN	DO	HI	IT	NO	OW	SO	WE
AS	EH	HO	LA	OF	OX	TA	YE

TOP TIP Like hooking, if you can tag with a premium square involved, then all the better!

MAKING 3 OR MORE WORDS IN ONE MOVE

You may be able to tag twice in one move, to make **3** words in one move.

Look at this situation in the top right-hand corner of the board later on during a game.

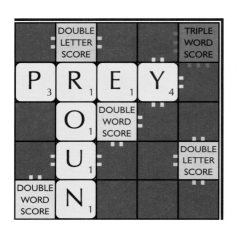

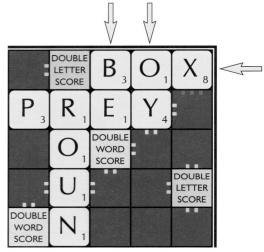

Player 1 has just put **PREY** through the **R** of **ROUND** to make a **DW** score.

This is the other player's rack:

Player 2 spots the chance to reach the **TW** score square, and tags **BOX** for 45 points.

BOX	(3 + 1 + 8) x 3	=	36
BE	(3 + 1)	=	4
OY	(1 + 4)	=	5
	Total score:		45pts

Not bad for little words!

40

Here is an example of another double tag making 3 words at once, including the **X** on a **TL** score square twice in one move!

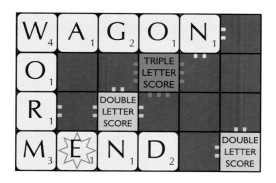

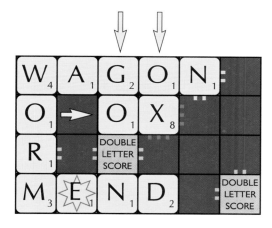

Player 1 has just played the letters **AGON** making **WAGON** for a **DW** score of 18 points.

Player 2 then tags **OX** across for 25pts
+ **GO** down for   3pts
+ **OX** down for   25pts

Total score: 53pts

An excellent score for just playing 2 letters.

Try to tag high-value letters on Triple Letter score squares so they are tripled twice by being part of two words.

We have seen single tags and double tags but you can also have treble tags, and even quadruple tags.

Look at this treble tag:

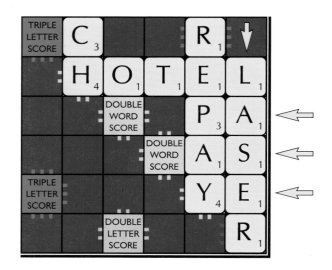

Player 1 played **HOTEL**

Player 2 added **REPAY** through **HOTEL**

Player 1 placed the letters **ASER** making:

LASER (**TW** score) (6 x 3) =	18
PA	5
AS	2
YE	5
Total score:	30pts

Here is a quadruple tag:

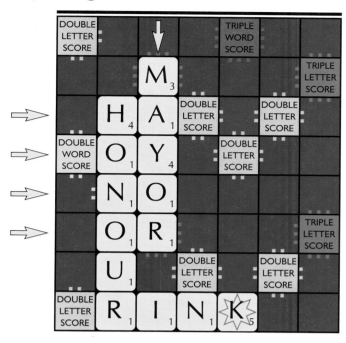

Player 1 opened with **INK** (14). Player 2 hooked **HONOUR**(18) +**RINK** (8)

Player 1 tagged **MAYOR** making **5 words** at once!

MAYOR	$(9 + 1 + 4 + 1 + 3)$ =	18
HA	$(4 + 1)$ =	5
OY	$(1 + 4)$ =	5
NO	$(1 + 1)$ =	2
OR	$(1 + 3)$ =	4
	Total score:	34pts

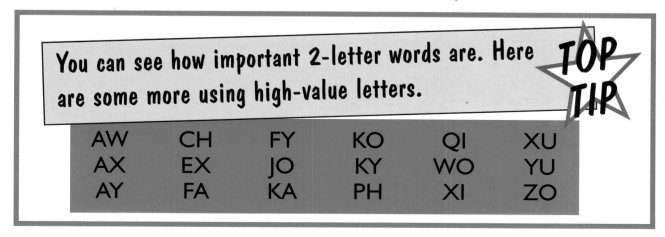

You can see how important 2-letter words are. Here are some more using high-value letters.

TOP TIP

AW	CH	FY	KO	QI	XU
AX	EX	JO	KY	WO	YU
AY	FA	KA	PH	XI	ZO

Many of these 2-letter words have weird and wonderful meanings, but they are **all allowable words** in Scrabble. Each one is very, very useful in making high-scoring moves, especially those including **J**, **X**, **Q** and **Z**.

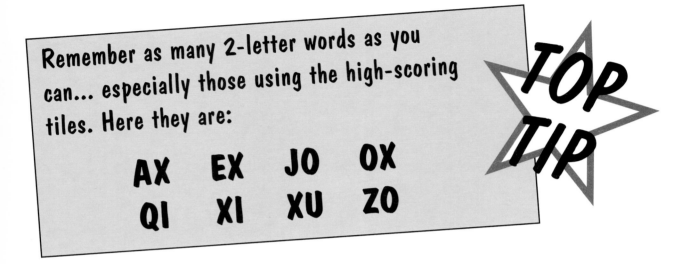

Remember as many 2-letter words as you can... especially those using the high-scoring tiles. Here they are:

AX   EX   JO   OX
QI   XI   XU   ZO

TOP TIP

There is a full list of **2-letter** words and their meanings at the back of the book.

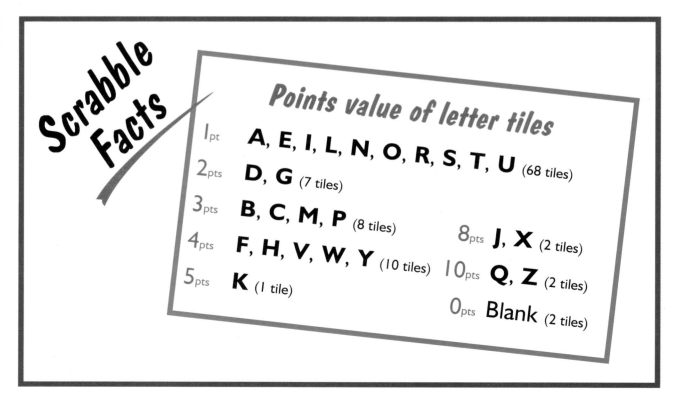

Scrabble Facts

Points value of letter tiles

1 pt	A, E, I, L, N, O, R, S, T, U (68 tiles)	
2 pts	D, G (7 tiles)	
3 pts	B, C, M, P (8 tiles)	8 pts J, X (2 tiles)
4 pts	F, H, V, W, Y (10 tiles)	10 pts Q, Z (2 tiles)
5 pts	K (1 tile)	0 pts Blank (2 tiles)

Fill in the spaces with tag words, making the arrowed scoring words with the one move.

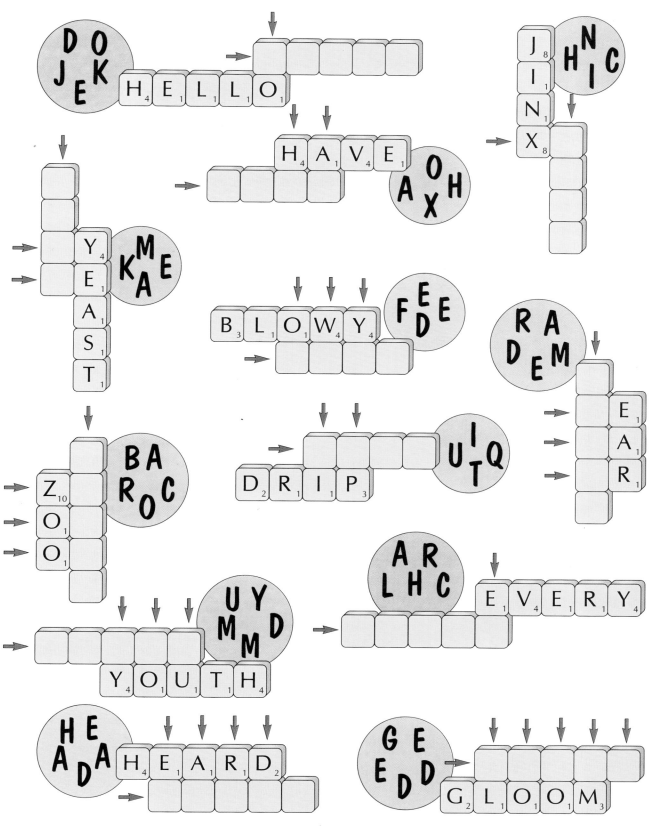

45

Try using the rack to tag a word which altogether forms 5 words at once (shown by the arrows).

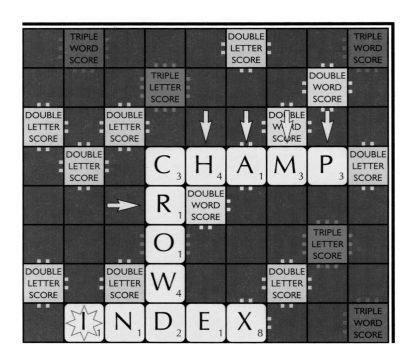

Target score: 33pts

Now try this rack to tag a word which altogether forms 3 words at once (shown by the arrows).

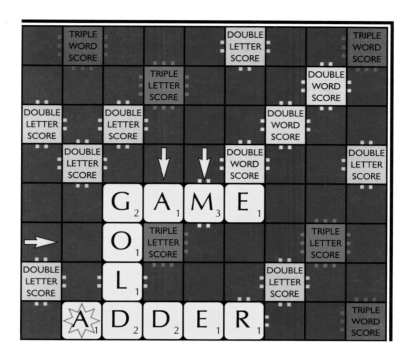

Target score: 65pts

PUZZLE BREAK

I T X
A A A B C E R T

A E
E I M O O R T X

Fill each shape with words using these letter tiles from your set. Use the
2-letter list at the back of the book.

Use the clues to change the word on the left into a new word on the right.
Both words have the same letters.

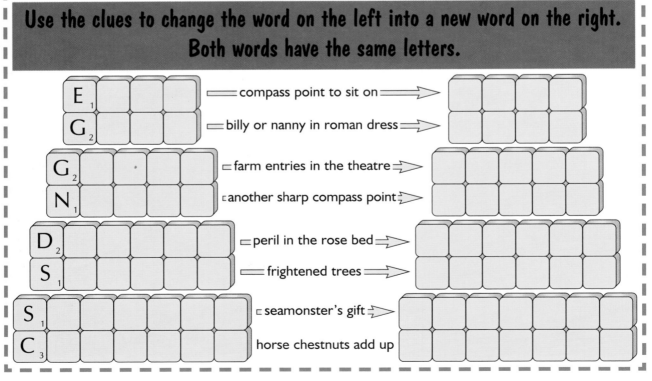

E

G

compass point to sit on

billy or nanny in roman dress

G

N

farm entries in the theatre

another sharp compass point

D

S

peril in the rose bed

frightened trees

S

C

seamonster's gift

horse chestnuts add up

48

GBRREOEWNN = G^BR^RE^OE^WN^N

Can you spot the 2 merged words in each set of letters? One letter is not used in each set. Put these in the last boxes and then jumble them to make a food.

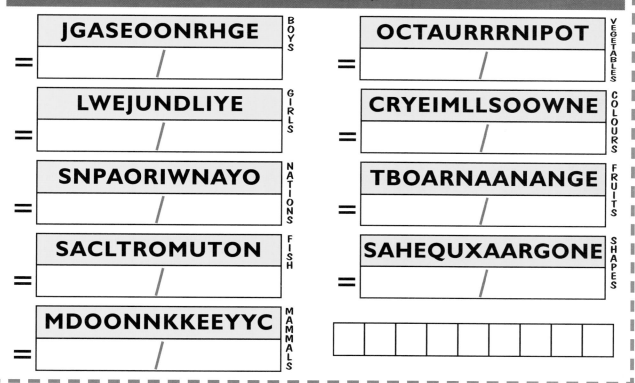

= JGASEOONRHGE /   BOYS

= LWEJUNDLIYE /   GIRLS

= SNPAORIWNAYO /   NATIONS

= SACLTROMUTON /   FISH

= MDOONNKKEEYYC /   MAMMALS

= OCTAURRRNIPOT /   VEGETABLES

= CRYEIMLLSOOWNE /   COLOURS

= TBOARNAANANGE /   FRUITS

= SAHEQUXAARGONE /   SHAPES

Jumble the letters in each sector to make the name of a kind of animal.

Put the first letter of each animal in the middle spaces — to spell another!

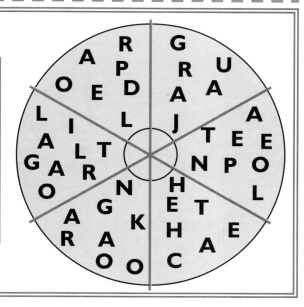

49

TOP TEN TILES

There are 100 tiles in a Scrabble set, but 10 of them should make your eyes light up when you pick them from the bag! These are the top ten:

 Never waste any of these tiles — aim for a score of at least 25 to 30 points when you play a word including one of them.

★ Play always on **DL** or **TL** squares, and, if possible, in **DW** or **TW** scores.

★ Remember **JO**, **XI**, **AX**, **EX**, **OX**, **QI**, **XU** and **ZO** for tagging.

★ Obviously, look out for the 4 **U**'s or use a blank as a **U**.

★ If a **U** is on the board already, try and use it as quickly as you can. Don't hang on to your **Q** for ages.

★ If all the **U**'s have been played, and you can't link your **Q**, then use a go to exchange it along with a couple of letters.

- ★ There are 2 useful **3-letter** words with a **Q** – **QAT** (a shrub) and **QUA** (acting as). Also remember the colour **AQUA** (useful to hook on to if **QUA** has been played).

- ★ Two words with a **Q** and no **U** are **QADI** and **QWERTY** (a judge and the arrangement of letters on a keyboard). And don't forget **QINTAR** and **QASIDA**.

- ★ Only worth 1 point but just about the most valuable letter!

- ★ Use **S** for hooking every time to make 2 plural words in one move.

- ★ Keep **S**'s at the right-hand end of your rack, and jumble the rest to make a **6-letter** word +**S** as a **7-letter** 'All Out' bonus, hooked on to the end of an already-played word.

- ★ Never waste an **S** in the middle or beginning of a word (unless it's an 'All Out' bonus).

- ★ Worth no points at all, but the most useful tile of the lot!

- ★ Hang on to it, to act as an **S**, or a **U** with a **Q**.

- ★ Best of all, use your imagination to combine with your other 6 tiles to make an 'All Out' bonus.

- ★ Never waste a blank in words not involving high-value letters on premium squares or in **DW** or **TW** scores.

If you pick a load of vowels and only 1 or 2 consonants then use a go to swap 4 or 5 tiles.

'ALL OUT BONUS'

Always look out for 7-letter words on your rack, especially if you have an **S** or a blank. Remember that you score 50 bonus points if you can play all 7 tiles in one move.

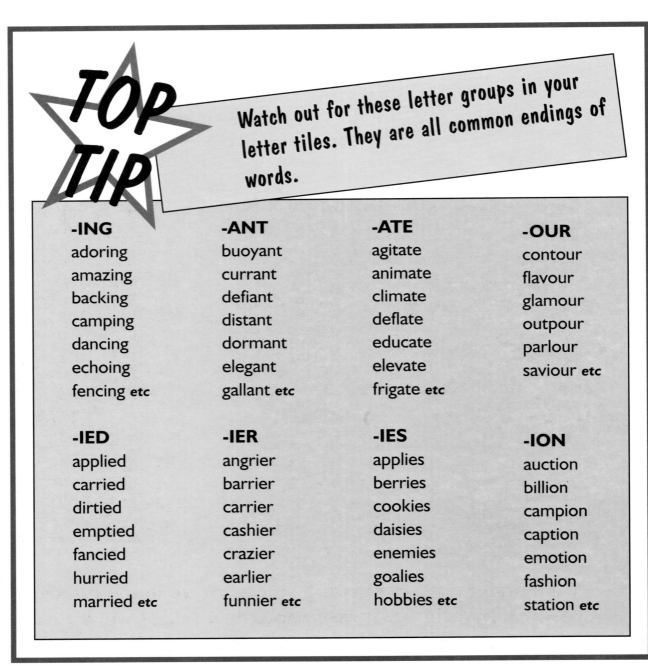

TOP TIP

Watch out for these letter groups in your letter tiles. They are all common endings of words.

-ING	**-ANT**	**-ATE**	**-OUR**
adoring	buoyant	agitate	contour
amazing	currant	animate	flavour
backing	defiant	climate	glamour
camping	distant	deflate	outpour
dancing	dormant	educate	parlour
echoing	elegant	elevate	saviour *etc*
fencing *etc*	gallant *etc*	frigate *etc*	

-IED	**-IER**	**-IES**	**-ION**
applied	angrier	applies	auction
carried	barrier	berries	billion
dirtied	carrier	cookies	campion
emptied	cashier	daisies	caption
fancied	crazier	enemies	emotion
hurried	earlier	goalies	fashion
married *etc*	funnier *etc*	hobbies *etc*	station *etc*

Try to work out these 'All Out Bonus' words (? = blank tile) – use your letter tiles to shuffle.

Now try and make the target scores in one move in the games on the next 8 pages. Earlier moves show how words can be made. Follow how the words have been played so far.

Target score: 50

First move:	**RAG**
Second move:	**DRAG/DATED**
Third move:	**THEY**
Fourth move:	**LEND**

Number of words to make: 2

Hook the colour of mud on to another word to make this score.

GAME 2

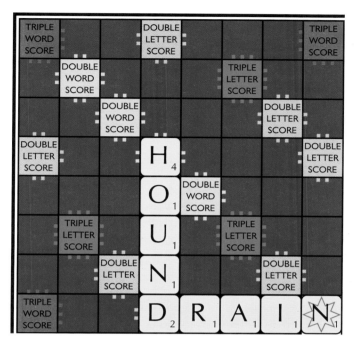

Target score: 43

First move: **RAIN**
Second move: **DRAIN/HOUND**

Number of words to make: 3

You're looking for something nobody likes paying, a word used to show laughter and a beast of burden.

55

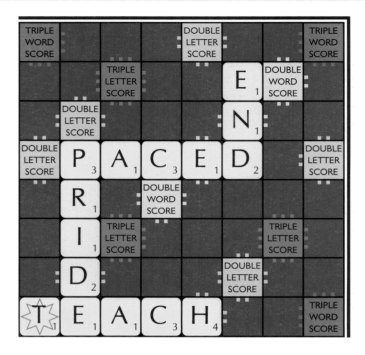

Target score: 68

First move:	**TEACH**
Second move:	**RIDE**
Third move:	**PRIDE/PACE**
Fourth move:	**PACED/END**

Number of words to make: 1

Use that Q carefully!

GAME 4

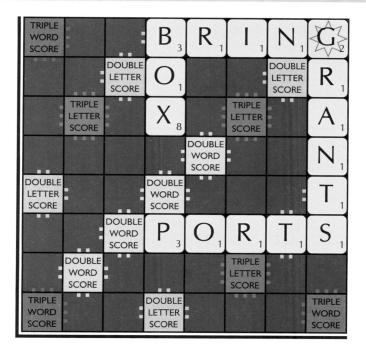

Target score: 98

First move:	**RING**
Second move:	**GRANT**
Third move:	**PORTS/GRANTS**
Fourth move:	**BOX/BRING**

Number of words to make: 4

A **zo** is an animal that is a cross between a yak and a cow, found in the Himalayas. This should help you find the answer!

57

Target score: 86

First move: **POET**
Second move: **PIN**

Number of words to make: 2

TOP TIP

If you have 4 consonants and 3 vowels keep shuffling your tiles to try to find a 7-letter word to score that 50-point bonus.

GAME 6

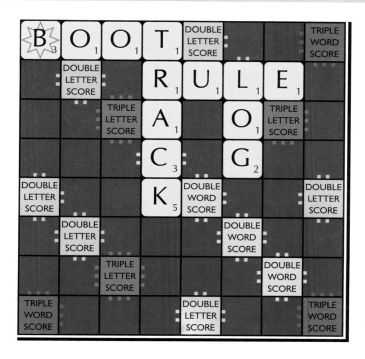

Target score: 50

First move: **BOOT**
Second move: **TRACK**
Third move: **RULE**
Fourth move: **LOG**

Number of words to make: 2

Don't forget that **X** can be used to make lots of 2-letter words.

59

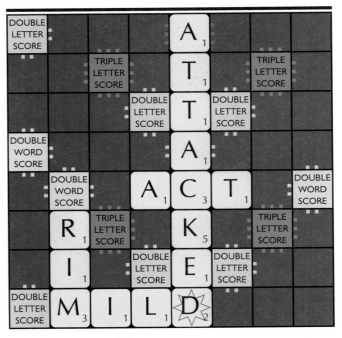

Target score: 48

First move:	**MILD**
Second move:	**ATTACKED** (Bonus Pts.)
Third move:	**RIM**
Fourth move:	**ACT**

Number of words to make: 2

GAME 8

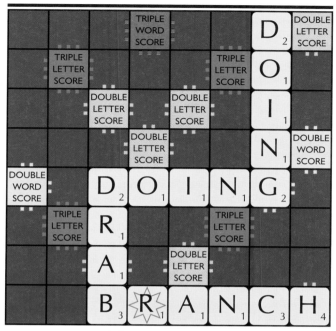

Target score: 61

First move:	**RANCH**
Second move:	**BRANCH/DRAB**
Third move:	**DOING**
Fourth move:	**DOING**

Number of words to make: 4

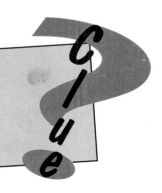

Elbows, hips and knees are all types of ?
Put this word on the board to make 3 more words.
Is it in the right place to reach the target score?

Solutions

3 quit, what; taxi, exam, team; just, jogs, jugs, most, mugs, must, oust; joust

4 red, doe, moo, bed, door, moor, oboe, robe, broom, rodeo; bedroom, boredom

5 ink, hen, ice, kit, cent, chin, kite, neck, think, thick, ketch, tench; kitchen, thicken

6 aim, jay, jam, may, yam

7 cow, wick, wok

8 juice

10 trick, relax, quack

11 bronze, awhile, chalky

12
```
      C        F              K
   A R M    T O Y        G E M
      Y        X              Y
```
tip, act, dream, lilac, related, shingle, residents (ICELAND)

13 Wellington, green, Jupiter, Dalmatians, Andrew, Paddington, yacht, Sicily, ladybird, Moon (CORNET)
jewel, ditch, camel, hedge, joked, laugh, stamp, catch, leave (WHALE)

14 bare, care, dare, fare, hare, mare, pare, rare, ware; band, hand, land, rand, wand; fair, hair, lair, pair; bear, dear, fear, gear, hear, near, pear, rear, wear; aware, glare; bland, brand, gland, grand; chair; clear

15 card, care, carp, cart;
cared, cargo, carol, carry, carve;
carbon, career, carpet, carrot, carved;
ford, fork, form, fort;
force, forge, forty, forum;
forbid, forget, formal, format

16 tramp, talent, custard, crocodile, microwave, policeman, abandon, recorder, exported, pharmacy, afternoon

18 much, juice, hurl, jump

19 quick, quin, cheque, quiche, quail

21 check, ache, make, peach

23 party, tyre, cried, crazy, created

24
```
   D A Y    A S H    H O T
   U        A        E      U
   O A K    E L M    R I B
```
add, sag, dance, cider, ocean, gallery, notices, snoozed, demanding (DANDELION)

25 William Shakespeare, Charles Dickens, J/X, Laurel/Hardy, Mercury/Venus, Blue Peter, Q/Z (ORANGE)
level, banjo, axes, acorn, habit, into, being, saved, educate, leaning, bishops, jubilee

28 brick, crate

29 jelly, growl

30 moved, rapid, five, hymn, jam, mice, begin, craze, mend, oily, banjo, zoo

31 stag, queens, miser, taxis, skate, posed, grown, widen, hilly, lorry, poked

32 know, flank

33 dwarf, what

34 chief, flake

36
```
   T      B      O        H
   I      A   V  E   R  Y
   D I S  C  E      M
   Y      K  R      N
```
keen/knee, hoes/shoe, cheap/peach, below/elbow, vowels/wolves, hornet/throne, general/enlarge, scented/descent

37 daisy/tulip, scarlet/purple, thrush/robin, giraffe/rabbit, Venus/Pluto, August/October, bread/bacon, spruce/beech, apricot/cherry (BADMINTON)
pigeon, lapwing, osprey, vulture, eagle, raven, (PLOVER)

45 joked, inch, hoax, make, feed, cobra, quit, dream, dummy, larch, ahead, edged

46 rodeo, ho, ad, me, po

47 foxy, ax, my

48
```
            A        E      O
         C A T    E X T R A
         T A X    M   O  I
         R I B
         E
```
east/seat, goat/toga, gates/stage, north/thorn, danger/garden, scared/cedars, serpent/present, conkers/reckons

49 Jason/George, Wendy/Julie, Spain/Norway, salmon/trout, monkey/donkey, carrot/turnip, crimson/yellow, banana/orange, square/hexagon (CHOCOLATE)
jaguar, antelope, cheetah, kangaroo, alligator, leopard (JACKAL)

53 attempt, cabbage, diamond, gazelle, kittens, ceiling, biscuit, wrinkle (winkler, warlike), novelty, problem (blooper)

54 brown(39), blend(11)

55 tax(20), ha(5), ox(18)

56 quiet(68)

57 zooms(52), zo(21), ox(9), sports(16)

58 careful(74), pine(12)

59 ex(25), ox(25)

60 tractor(36), trim(12)

61 joint(40), jo(17), oi(2), in(2)